Contents

C000005459

Introcution

The Mental Warm-up Activities provide a structured scheme of work for developing mental mathematics strategies. The daily activities have been written to practise key mental maths skills, and address these using a variety of tactics:

- practising pre-requisite skills (e.g. partitioning numbers: 8 is 7 and 1, 6 and 2, 5 and 3, 4 and 4)

- building on two or more of these skills to develop a new strategy (e.g. adding 17 + 8 by partitioning 8 into 3 and 5, and knowing that 17 + 3 = 20)

- practising and extending known strategies (e.g. 27 + 8 =)

- using known strategies as pre-requisites for a new set of strategies, (e.g. related to a different operation)

- developing a 'memory bank' of key facts (e.g. addition bonds to 10, doubles to 10)

- using key facts to develop further strategies (e.g. 3 + 3 = 6 so 3 + 4 = 7)

How to use this book

To allow the teacher flexibility, the book is broken down into two sections:

Unit specific activities

For each Number Unit there are two whole class activities. Some of these relate directly to skills or sub-skills for that Unit. Some activities practise more general skills, and these will develop in strands throughout the book (a skills chart mapping this development is included on pages 70 and 71). Often the two activities provided will be enough to cover the work required for that Unit.

Activity bank

For number Units that last longer than two days, or for shape, space and measures Units, the teacher can select supplementary activities from the

Bank provided at the back of the book. The Activity Bank includes a wide variety of activities that address key skills under topic headings (e.g. counting, addition, place-value). The activities in the bank can be used at any time alongside any topic, and often you will wish to revisit them throughout the year.

Together, these two types of activity will provide enough activities for one warm-up every day.

The activities

The mental activities are of three types:

Open-ended

These are activities where there may be several ways of getting a 'right' answer. Often a key benefit of the activity will be the discussion which the children have with you and each other about which strategies they have used. This is a good opportunity to go through several different ways of doing something with the whole class, so that different methods or techniques are shared and discussed.

Closed

These activities have one correct answer and usually, one preferred strategy to use. So, for example, when adding 9 to a 2-digit number, the activity may practise the specific technique of adding 10 and taking one away.

Memorising

These activities are designed to help children memorise a particular set of number facts, e.g. doubles of numbers to 10, addition bonds. Eventually each child will have a set of memorised facts that they know by heart. Certain key activities appear several times during the book to help reinforce these skills.

Generic activities

Most of the activities use similar formats and structures from Unit to Unit, and children will become familiar with these. These 'generic' activities are described in more detail on pages vi to viii.

Also included in each unit are a word of the week, a number of the week or a shape of the week. These can be used to develop children's use of the language and vocabulary of number both spoken ('tell me something about this week's number') and written ('write three things about this week's shape').

The number of the week can be used to develop mental dexterity, consolidate concepts and skills studied in a given Number Unit, and to develop the use and understanding of the language of number. For each number some sample tasks and facts are given.

The shape of the week can be used to increase awareness of the properties of shape and space, and to encourage the use of the associated language.

The word of the week can be used to develop use and understanding of the vocabulary of mathematics, and to consolidate language associated with the Unit being studied. Sometimes the 'word of the week' relates to vocabulary in the relevant Unit, sometimes the word is included to rehearse vocabulary met in the past or to introduce new vocabulary. Children should be encouraged to both hear the word being used in different contexts, and to use the word in responses and statements.

Working partners

At the beginning of the year (or each term), place the children in pairs as 'working partners'. The pairs do not necessarily have to be matched in ability – two children of different abilities can help each other. Over time the children will become used to working together, and a 'regular' partner will save you time when setting up the activities.

Generic activities

Many of the activities throughout this book follow common formats and structures. This will enable you to quickly set up and run a particular activity, and over time, the children will become used to the 'rules' involved. The 'generic' activities are described here in more detail.

Cross it out

- The children work with their partners. They write two numbers on a piece of paper. The numbers should match a certain criterion (e.g. less than 10).
- The teacher generates numbers at random (e.g. by selecting cards from a shuffled set).
- The teacher chooses a child to perform an operation on the card (e.g. saying the pair to make ten).
- The children can cross out one of their numbers if it matches the answer.
- The first pair to cross out both numbers wins.

My mistake

- The teacher writes two or three number sentences on the board (e.g. pairs to 10) one or more of which are incorrect.
- Allow the children a few minutes to decide which are incorrect.
- Go through them on the board, asking different children whether each is correct or incorrect.

Round the class

- The teacher points to a child and says a number.
- That child responds with a new number (e.g. by counting on one, or back ten).
- The first child chooses another who continues the count, and so on.
- A good rule is to let boys choose girls and girls choose boys.

Show me

- Children work with their partners. Each pair has a set of number cards.
- The teacher calls out several calculations and the pairs match the answers with their cards (they can make 2-digit numbers by holding two cards together).

Teddy throw

- Use a teddy bear, or other soft toy.
- The teacher passes the teddy to one child, and says a number.
- That child performs an operation on that number (e.g. add ten), and passes the teddy to a new child.
- The second child performs the same operation on the new number, and so on.

Counting chorus

- Divide the class into four large groups, and name them (e.g. by colour or animal).
- Give one group a starting number. They count on (e.g. in ones, twos or tens).
- After a few moments point to another group, who take over the count.
- Continue around the groups.

Fast fingers

- Give the children a simple calculation or number operation.
- As quickly as possible they match the answer by holding up fingers.
- Repeat, maintaining a brisk pace.

Grid

- Draw a two-row grid on the board, with appropriate numbers in the top row.
- In pairs, the children perform an operation on each number (e.g. adding ten).
- Go through the grid on the board, asking different pairs for their answer, before writing it on the grid.

Guess what?

- One child stands at the front, with a number card (or other, e.g. coin) stuck to her back.
- The rest of the class are invited to give clues to help her guess the number. Encourage creative clues.
- The first child makes guesses, each one costing her 1p (keep a tally on the board). Limit it to a maximum of five or ten guesses.
- How much does she owe by the time she guesses?

Odd one out

- Write three calculations on the board, one of which is different in some way from the others (e.g. it has a different answer).
- The children work in pairs to find the answer and decide which is the odd one out.
- Choose different pairs to answer, and explain their reasoning.
- Repeat for different calculations.

Lose a life

- The children work in pairs, each pair with three cubes and a set of number cards.
- Give the class a calculation, and allow the pairs a few moments to decide the answer.
- Each pair holds up cards to match the answer.
- Any pair who answers incorrectly 'lose a life' and gives up a cube.
- Repeat. Who has 'lives' left after several rounds?

 N1 Numbers to 20

Teddy throw

Counting back in ones

Pass the teddy to one child, saying a 1-digit number, e.g. *eight*. They take the teddy and pass it to another child saying the number one less i.e. *seven*. That child passes the teddy on to another child, saying the number one less, i.e. *six*. Keep passing the teddy like this.

Counting chorus

Counting to 20

Divide the class into four large groups and assign each group a colour or animal. Point to a group, say a number and ask them to start counting in ones, e.g. *six, seven, eight*, … After a few moments point to another group, who take over the count. After a few moments point to another group …

Practise so that the change-overs are smooth.

Number of the week

Sample tasks
- Read and say the number.
- Count forwards in ones from one to the number.
- Count backwards in ones from the number.
- Count forwards in ones from the number.
- Show six objects, e.g. coins.

Sample facts
- it is more than 4
- it is less than 8
- it is 2 more than 4
- it is the number of eggs in a box
- it is the third even number

N2 Ordering

Fast fingers!

Number names up to ten
Flash cards labelled one, two, three, ... ten

Choose a card and hold it up (don't say the number). The children match it with fingers, as fast as they can.

Repeat, maintaining a brisk pace.

Cross it out

Counting to 20
Cubes

Each pair writes two numbers between 1 and 20 on a piece of paper. Take one or two handfuls of cubes. Choose a child to count how many, and write the number on the board. Any pair with the matching number can cross it out.

The winners are the first to cross out both their numbers.

Shape of the week

square

Sample facts
- it is a flat shape
- it has 4 sides
- it has 4 corners
- its sides are all the same length

N3 Addition

Grid

Ten more

Draw a 'ten more' grid on the board. In the top row write 1-digit numbers at random. Allow the children a few minutes to find ten more than each number, to go in the bottom row.

Ten more		
6	2	7
16		

Go through the grid on the board asking different pairs for their answers.

Show me

Adding two 1-digit numbers
Number cards (0 to 9), one set per pair

Give the children different additions, and ask them to choose cards to match the answer. When you say: *Show me!* they all hold up their cards. For example:

What is the total of … three and two, seven and four, one and eight, two and seven, four and five.

Number of the week

Sample tasks
- Read and say the number.
- Hop four times.
- Write the number '4'.
- Count forwards in ones from the number.
- Show four objects, e.g. cubes.

Sample facts
- it is more than 3
- it is a 1-digit number
- it is 3 add 1
- it is the number of sides on a square, corners on a rectangle
- it is the number of seasons in a year

N4 Addition

Guess what?

Numbers to 20
Number cards (1 to 20)

Choose a child and stick a number card to her back. The rest of the class give clues to help her guess the number, e.g. *It is between 10 and 20.*

Each guess costs her 1p. How much does she owe by the time she guesses?

Odd one out

Adding two 1-digit numbers
Write three additions on the board, two of which have the same answer, e.g. 5 + 6 = , 10 + 2 = , 4 + 4 + 3 =.

Allow the pairs a few minutes to decide which is the 'odd one out'.

Repeat for different additions.

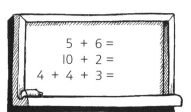

$$5 + 6 =$$
$$10 + 2 =$$
$$4 + 4 + 3 =$$

Word of the week

between

Sample tasks
- Say a number between 5 and 10.
- What is the difference between a square and a cube?
- Stand between me and the door.

Sample facts
- 6 is between 5 and 7
- there are no even numbers between 8 and 10
- there are 6 numbers between 5 and 12

N5 Subtraction

Lose a life

Doubling
Number cards (1 to 10), one set per pair, cubes

Give each pair three cubes, representing three 'lives'. Say an addition double, e.g. *What is three add three?* Each pair chooses cards to match the answer and, on your cue, holds them up.

Any pair who answers incorrectly loses a life and must give you a cube.

Repeat.

My mistake

Taking away from a number up to 10
Write two subtractions on the board, one of which is incorrect. The children work together in pairs to decide which one is incorrect. After a few minutes choose different pairs to answer. Choose one pair to re-write the subtraction correctly.

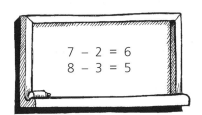

$$7 - 2 = 6$$
$$8 - 3 = 5$$

Number of the week

3

Sample tasks
- Clap 3 times.
- Write our number.
- Add our number to 5, to 10, ...
- Take our number away from 5, from 7, ...
- Say three consecutive (next-door) numbers, e.g. 5, 6, 7.

Sample facts
- it is 4 take away 1, 5 take away 2, ...
- it is 1 add 2
- it is the second odd number
- it is the number of sides of a triangle
- it is the number of wheels on a tricycle

Money

Round the class

Adding 1p to amounts
Cubes

Point to a child and say an amount, e.g. 2p. That child responds by saying 1p more, i.e. 3p. They choose another child (boys choose girls and vice versa), who says 1p more. The first child to say an amount that can be matched with another coin (i.e. 5p) takes a cube.

Repeat, starting at a different amount, e.g. 6p.

Grid

Coin recognition
Draw a 2 × 5 grid on the board. In the top row write different amounts at random. Allow the children a few minutes to find ways of matching each amount with different coins, to go in the bottom row.

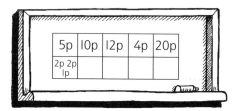

Go through the grid on the board asking different pairs for their answers.

Shape of the week

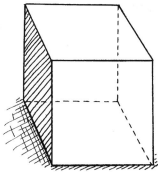

Sample facts
• it has 6 faces
• its faces are all squares
• it has 12 edges
• it has 8 corners (or vertices)
• some bricks are cube-shaped

N7 Numbers to 20

Teddy throw

Counting in tens

Pass the teddy to one child, saying: *ten*. They take the teddy and pass it to another child saying the number ten more i.e. *twenty*. That child passes the teddy on to another child, saying the number ten more, i.e. *thirty*. Keep passing the teddy like this.

Cross it out

Counting to 20

A mixed set of coins

Each pair writes two numbers between 1 and 20 on a piece of paper. Take one or two handfuls of coins. Choose a child to count how much, and write the total on the board. Any pair with the matching number can cross it out.

The winners are the first to cross out both their numbers.

Number of the week

15

Sample tasks
- Count in ones forwards to our number.
- Count in ones backwards from our number.
- Write our number.
- Say 5 less/5 more than our number.

Sample facts
- it is a 2-digit number
- it is halfway between 10 and 20
- it is an odd number
- it is 2 more than 13
- it is not less than 10

N8 Counting in twos

Fast fingers!

Adding two 1-digit numbers

Say a simple addition, e.g. *three and two more*. The children match the answers with fingers, as fast as they can.

Repeat, maintaining a brisk pace.

Round the class

Counting in twos
Cubes

Point to a child and say an even number, e.g. *two*. He responds by saying two more, i.e. *four*. He chooses another child (boys choose girls and vice versa), who says two more. The first child to say a number ending in zero (i.e. 10) takes a cube.

Repeat, starting at a different number, e.g. 12.

Word of the week

Sample tasks
- What is the name of this month?
- Say the months in order.
- What is the first month of the year?
- Which month comes after May?
- In which month is your birthday?

Sample facts
- there are 12 months in a year
- the winter months are December, January, February
- most months have 30 or 31 days
- the school year starts in September

(N9) Place-value

Counting chorus

Counting in twos

Divide the class into four large groups and assign each group a colour or animal. Point to a group, and ask them to start counting in twos, i.e. *two, four, six, ...* After a few moments point to another group, who take over the count. After a few moments point to another group ...

Practise so that the change-overs are smooth.

Jumping jellybean

Counting to 20
Number cards (1 to 20)

Choose a pair and deal them a card. One child jumps to match the card, while the other counts. Are they both correct?

Repeat.

Number of the week

Sample tasks
- Count in twos forwards to our number, and on from our number.
- Count in ones backwards from our number
- Write our number.
- What is 1 more/1 less than our number?
- Build our number with interlocking cubes.

Sample facts
- it is 10 add 2
- it is a 2-digit number
- it is between 10 and 15
- it is called a dozen
- it is the number of numbers on a clock-face
- it is the number of months in a year

N10 Subtraction

Guess what?

Numbers to 30
Number cards (20 to 30)

Choose a child and stick a number card to her back. The rest of the class give clues to help her guess the number, e.g. *It is between 20 and 30.*

Each guess costs her 1p. How much does she owe by the time she guesses?

Lose a life

Taking away from a number up to 10
Number cards (1 to 10), one set per pair, cubes

Give each pair three cubes, representing three 'lives'. Say a subtraction, e.g. *Six take away two leaves…?* Each pair chooses cards to match the answer and, on your cue, holds them up. Any pair who answers incorrectly loses a life and must give you a cube.

Repeat.

Shape of the week

{ **triangle** }

Sample facts
- it is a flat shape which has 3 straight sides
- it has 3 corners (vertices)
- you can fold a square piece of paper to make a triangle
- a triangle has one less side than a square
- some parts of roofs are triangle shaped

N11 Addition

Odd one out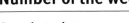

Taking away from a number up to 20
Write three subtractions on the board,
two of which have the same answer,
e.g. 13 – 4 = , 10 – 3 = , 11 – 2 =.

Allow the pairs a few minutes to decide
which is the 'odd one out'.

Repeat for different subtractions.

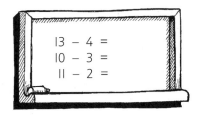

13 – 4 =
10 – 3 =
11 – 2 =

Show me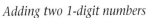

Adding two 1-digit numbers
Number cards (0 to 9), one set per pair

Give the children different additions, and ask them to choose cards to
match the answer. When you say: *Show me!* they all hold up their cards.
For example:

*What is the total of … three and two, seven and four, one and eight, two and
seven, four and five?*

Number of the week

5

Sample tasks
- Count in fives starting with our number.
- Add 1, 2, 3, … to our number.
- Add our number to 10, 5, …
- Say two numbers which make our number, e.g. 1 and 4.

Sample facts
- it is 1 less than 6
- it is 2 add 3
- it is the fifth number
- it is the number of fingers on one hand
- it is the number of toes on one foot

N12 Addition

My mistake

Adding two 1-digit numbers, crossing ten
Write two additions on the board, one
of which is incorrect, e.g. 8 + 6 = 13,
and 4 + 7 = 11. The children work
together in pairs to decide which one
is incorrect. After a few minutes
choose different pairs to answer. Choose one pair to re-write the addition
correctly.

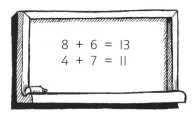

$$8 + 6 = 13$$
$$4 + 7 = 11$$

Teddy throw

Counting in tens
Pass the teddy to one child, saying a 1-digit number,
e.g. *eight*. They take the teddy and pass it to another
child saying the number ten more i.e. *eighteen*. That
child passes the teddy on to another child, saying the
number ten more, i.e. *twenty-eight*. Keep passing the teddy like this.

Number of the week

13

Sample tasks
- Add 1, 2, 3, ... to our number.
- Write our number.
- Write one more, three more than our number.
- How many more than 11 is our number?

Sample facts
- it is a 2-digit number
- it is 3 more than 10
- it is between 10 and 20
- it is an 'unlucky' number
- both digits are odd

 # N13 Money

Grid

Adding 10 to a teen number

Draw a 'ten more' grid on the board. In the top row write teen numbers at random. Allow the children a few minutes to find ten more than each number, to go in the bottom row.

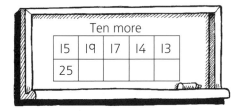

Ten more				
15	19	17	14	13
25				

Go through the grid on the board asking different pairs for their answers.

Fast fingers!

Coin recognition

A selection of coins (1p, 2p, 5p, 10p)

Hold up a coin, e.g. 2p. The children match the amount with fingers, as fast as they can.

Repeat for different coins, maintaining a brisk pace.

Repeat for holding up more than one coin.

Number of the week

Sample tasks
- Count in ones back from 20 to our number.
- Take our number away from 7, 3, 10, ...
- Add our number to 5, 12, 20, ...

Sample facts
- it is the first counting number
- it is odd
- it is the number after zero

Addition

Cross it out

Adding 10 to a 1-digit number
A dice

Each pair writes two numbers between 10 and 17 on a piece of paper. Throw the dice and choose a child to add 10. Any pair with the matching number can cross it out.

The winners are the first to cross out both their numbers.

Round the class

Addition pairs to 10
Point to a child and say a number, e.g. *nine*. He responds by saying the number to make 10, i.e. *one*. He chooses another child (boys choose girls and vice versa), and says a number, e.g. *three*. That child responds by saying the number to make 10, i.e. *seven*.

Continue around the class.

Number of the week

Sample tasks
- Count in 10s from our number to one hundred.
- Tell me two numbers which add to total our number, e.g. $4 + 6$, ...
- What makes our number with 3, with 8, ...?
- Add our number to 3, to 7, to 5, ...

Sample facts
- it is the tenth counting number
- it is the first 2-digit number
- it is 5 less than 15, ...
- it is the number of fingers on our hands, toes on our feet

N15 Numbers to 100

Jumping jellybean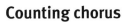

Counting to 20
A selection of coins (1p to 20p)

Choose a pair and give them a coin. One child jumps to match the amount, while the other counts. Are they both correct?

Repeat for different pairs. Try giving some pairs more than one coin.

...seventeen... eighteen...

Counting chorus

Counting in tens
Divide the class into four large groups and assign each group a colour or animal. Point to a group, and ask them to start counting in tens from a 1-digit number, e.g. *six, sixteen, twenty-six, ...* After a few moments point to another group, who take over the count. After a few moments point to another group ...

Practise so that the change-overs are smooth.

Number of the week

30

Sample tasks
- Count in fives to our number.
- Count in tens from our number.
- Subtract 10, 20, 30, from our number.
- Add 10, 20, 30, ... to our number.

Sample facts
- it is one of the 'tens' numbers
- it is between 20 and 40
- it is in the 'fives' and in the 'tens'
- it is the number of days in April, ...

Place-value

Lose a life

Addition pairs to 10
**Number cards (1 to 10),
one set per pair, cubes**

Give each pair three
cubes, representing
three 'lives'. Say a
number. e.g. *six*. Each
pair chooses the card to
make ten (i.e. 4) and, on your cue, holds it up. Any pair who answers
incorrectly loses a life and must give you a cube.

Repeat.

Guess what?

Numbers to 50
Number cards (20 to 50)

Choose a child and stick a number card to her back. The rest of the class
give clues to help her guess the number, e.g. *It has four tens.*

Each guess costs her 1p. How much does she owe by the time she
guesses?

Number of the week

Sample tasks
- Count in ones to our number.
- Count in twos to our number.
- Write 2 less/2 more than our number.
- Take 10 from our number.
- How many need to be added to our number to make 20?

Sample facts
- it is between 15 and 17
- it is not less than 10
- its digits total 7
- one of its digits is even, one is odd

 Addition

Odd one out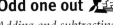

Adding and subtracting

Write three calculations on the board, two of which have the same answer, e.g. $3 + 10 =$, $5 + 9 =$, $23 - 10 =$.

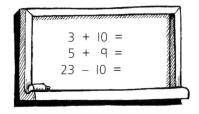

$$3 + 10 =$$
$$5 + 9 =$$
$$23 - 10 =$$

Allow the pairs a few minutes to decide which is the 'odd one out'.

Repeat for different calculations.

Teddy throw

Doubling

Pass the teddy to one child, saying a 1-digit number, e.g. *eight*. They take the teddy and double the number, i.e. *sixteen*. They pass the teddy to another child saying a new 1-digit number, e.g. *three*. That child doubles the number before passing the teddy on to another child, saying a new number. Keep passing the teddy like this.

Word of the week

Sample tasks
- What is the double of 5?
- Is 13 a double?
- What number doubled makes 10?
- Say the doubles in order, starting from 2.
- Is your house number a double?

Sample facts
- a double is two of a number, or twice a number
- double 10 is 20
- 8 is double 4, 6 is double 3, ...
- even numbers are doubles

Grid

Addition pairs to 10
Draw a 2 × 5 grid on the
board. In the top row write
1-digit numbers at random.
Allow the children a few
minutes to find the pair to
10 for each number, to go in
the bottom row. Go through the grid on the board asking different pairs
for their answers.

Pairs to ten				
5	3	7	q	2
5				

My mistake

*Adding two 1-digit numbers,
crossing 10*
Write two additions on the
board, one of which is incorrect,
e.g. 8 + 6 = 13, and 4 + 7 = 11.
The children work together in
pairs to decide which one is
incorrect. After a few minutes
choose different pairs to answer.

$$8+6 = 13$$
$$4+7 = 11$$

Choose one pair to re-write the addition correctly. Repeat.

Number of the week

7

Sample tasks
- What goes with 1, 2, 3, ... 7 to make 7?
- Say a pair of numbers which add to make 7.
- Count on from our number, in ones, to 20.
- Count back from our number in twos.
- What must be added to our number to make 10, 20?

Sample facts
- it is 1 + 6, 2 + 5, ...
- it is 8 take away 1, 9 take away 2, ...
- it is 3 less than 10
- it is the number of days in a week
- it is the number of sides on a 50p coin

Show me

Adding two 1-digit numbers
Number cards (0 to 9), one set per pair

Give the children different additions, and ask them to choose cards to match the answer. When you say: *Show me!* they all hold up their cards. For example:

What is the total of … five and two, six and four, one and eight, two and seven, four and five?

Fast fingers!

Addition pairs to 10
Each child holds up ten fingers. Say a number, e.g. *seven*. The children fold down that many fingers and say how many are still standing, i.e. *three!*

Repeat for different 1-digit numbers, maintaining a brisk pace.

Number of the week

Sample tasks
- Say a pair of numbers which add to make our number.
- What must be added to our number to make 20?
- Count in ones from our number to 30.
- Count in twos from 1 to our number.
- Write 1 more/1 less than our number.

Sample facts
- it is 3 + 6, 1 + 8, 7 + 2, …
- it is 10 − 1, 11 − 2, …
- it is the largest 1-digit number
- it is 1 less than 10

N20 Addition

Round the class

Counting in twos
Cubes

Point to a child and say an even number, e.g. *twelve*. That child responds by saying two more, i.e. *fourteen*. They choose another child (boys choose girls and vice versa), who says two more. The first child to say a number ending in zero (i.e. 20) takes a cube.

Repeat, starting at a different number, e.g. 4.

Cross it out

Adding 10 to a 1-digit number
Number cards (1 to 10)

Each pair writes two numbers between 10 and 20 on a piece of paper. Select a card and choose a child to add 10. Any pair with the matching number can cross it out.

The winners are the first to cross out both their numbers.

Shape of the week

(circle)

Sample facts
- it is a flat shape
- it has one curved side
- many objects have a circle shape, e.g. a sticker, a disc
- it is different from squares, triangles, rectangles, because they have straight sides

N21 Odd and even

Counting chorus

Counting in twos

Divide the class into four large groups and
assign each group a colour or animal.
Point to a group, and ask them to start
counting in twos, i.e. *two, four, six, ...*
After a few moments point to another
group, who take over the count. After
a few moments point to another
group ...

Practise so that the change-
overs are smooth.

Guess what?

Numbers to 20

Number cards (1 to 20)

Choose a child and stick a number card to his back. The rest of the class
give clues to help him guess the number, e.g. *It is even.*

Each guess costs him 1p. How much does he owe by the time he guesses?

Word of the week

Sample tasks
- Is 8 an even number?
- What is the next even number after 14?
- Say the even numbers, in order, starting at 2.
- Is the date today an even number?
- Do you have an even number of brothers and sisters?

Sample facts
- even numbers are the 'twos'
- numbers which are not even are odd
- even numbers have a units digit of 0, 2, 4, 6 or 8
- the first even number is 2

(N22) Number patterns

Lose a life 🗣️

Odd and even

Number cards (1 to 10), one set per pair, cubes

Give each pair three cubes, representing three 'lives'. Say either 'even' or 'odd'. Each pair chooses a card to match and, on your cue, holds it up. Any pair who answers incorrectly loses a life and must give you a cube.

Repeat.

Cross it out 🗣️

Adding 10 to a 1-digit number

Number cards (1 to 10)

Each pair writes two numbers between 10 and 20 on a piece of paper. Select a card and choose a child to add 10. Any pair with the matching number can cross it out. The winners are the first to cross out both their numbers.

Number of the week

(14)

Sample tasks
- Count in twos from 2 to our number.
- Count in twos forwards from our number.
- What must be added to our number to make 20?
- Say two numbers which make our number, e.g. 10 + 4.
- Take away 1, 3, 2, 5 ... from our number.

Sample facts
- it is between 10 and 20
- it is 4 and 10
- it is the number of days in two weeks
- it is even – the seventh even number
- it is double 7

(N23) Ordering

Jumping jellybean

Counting to 20
Number cards (10 to 20)

Choose a pair and give them a card.
One child jumps to match the card,
while the other counts. Are they
both correct?

Repeat for different pairs.

Odd one out

Adding and subtracting
Write three calculations on the board,
two of which have the same answer,
e.g. 16 + 10 = , 37 − 10 = , 15 + 11 =.

Allow the pairs a few minutes to
decide which is the 'odd one out'.

Repeat for different calculations.

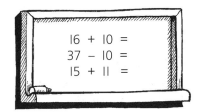

$16 + 10 =$
$37 - 10 =$
$15 + 11 =$

Number of the week

Sample tasks
- Count in twos forwards from our number.
- Say a pair of numbers which add to make our number.
- What must be added to 3, to 7, ... to make our number?
- Add 1, 3, 10, 2, ... to our number.
- Take 1, 3, 4, 7 ... from our number.

Sample facts
- it is double 4
- it is the fourth even number
- it is 1 + 7, 2 + 6, 3 + 5, 4 + 4, ...
- it is 2 less than 10
- it is the number of legs on an octopus, on a spider
- it is one more than the number of days in a week

Ordering

Teddy throw

Counting back in ones

Pass the teddy to one child, saying a 2-digit number,
e.g. *sixty-eight*. They take the teddy and say the number
one less, i.e. *sixty-seven*. They pass the teddy to another
child who says one less, i.e. *sixty-six*. Keep passing the
teddy like this.

Grid

Addition pairs to 10

Draw a 2 × 5 grid on the
board. In the top row write
1-digit numbers at random.
Allow the children a few
minutes to find the pair to 10
for each number, to go in the bottom row.

Bonds to ten				
5	3	7	9	2
5				

Go through the grid on the board asking different pairs for their answers.

Shape of the week

Sample facts
- it is a flat shape
- it has 4 straight sides
- it has 4 corners (vertices)
- it has one more side than a triangle
- it usually has two longer sides and two shorter sides
- many shapes around us are rectangle shaped, e.g. table-tops, book covers

N25 Addition and money

My mistake

Adding three 1-digit numbers

Write two additions on the board, one of which is incorrect, e.g. $3 + 5 + 5 = 13$, and $2 + 7 + 7 = 17$. The children work together in pairs to decide which one is incorrect. After a few minutes choose different pairs to answer. Choose one pair to re-write the addition correctly.

Show me

Addition pairs to 10

Number cards (0 to 10), one set per pair

Give the children different numbers, and ask them to choose cards to make ten. When you say: *Show me!* they all hold up their cards. For example:

What goes with... five, seven, nine, one, ... to make ten?

Number of the week

20

Sample tasks
- Count in twos, forwards from 2 to our number, and backwards from 20.
- Count in fives to our number.
- Count in tens from our number.
- Say a pair of numbers which add to our number, e.g. 6 and 14.
- Add our number to 4, to 8, to 1, ...

Sample facts
- it is an even number – the tenth
- it is double 10
- it is $1 + 19$, $2 + 18$, $3 + 17$, ...
- it is the number of pennies equal to two 10p coins
- it is the total number of toes on two people

 N26 Addition

Fast fingers!

Addition pairs to 10
Each child holds up ten fingers. Say a number,
e.g. *seven*. The children fold down that many
fingers and say how many are still standing, i.e.
three!

Repeat for different 1-digit numbers,
maintaining a brisk pace.

Odd one out

Adding and subtracting
Write three calculations on the board,
two of which have the same answer,
e.g. $4 + 5 =$, $3 + 6 =$, $12 - 2 =$.

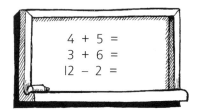

$$4 + 5 =$$
$$3 + 6 =$$
$$12 - 2 =$$

Allow the pairs a few minutes to decide
which is the 'odd one out'.

Repeat for different calculations.

Shape of the week

cuboid

Sample facts
- it is a box shape
- it has 6 flat faces
- its faces are either squares or
  rectangles
- it has 8 corners (vertices)
- it has 12 edges $(4 + 4 + 4)$

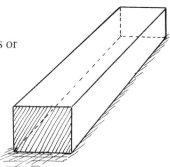

N27 Addition/subtraction

Round the class

Counting in tens
Cubes

Point to a child and say a number, e.g. *twenty-two*. He responds by saying ten more, i.e. *thirty-two*. He chooses another child (boys choose girls and vice versa), who says ten more. The first child to say a number over 100 takes a cube.

Repeat, starting at a different number, e.g. *four*.

Lose a life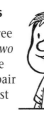

Taking away from a number up to 10
Number cards (1 to 10), one set per pair, cubes

Give each pair three cubes, representing three 'lives'. Say a subtraction, e.g. *six take away two is…* Each pair chooses the card to match the answer and, on your cue, holds it up. Any pair who answers incorrectly loses a life and must give you a cube.

Repeat.

Number of the week

17

Sample tasks
- Count in ones backwards from our number, to zero.
- Count in ones forwards from our number, to 30.
- Add 3, 1, 10 to our number.
- Split our number up into tens and ones.
- Take 1, 2, 0, 3, 7 from our number.

Sample facts
- it is an odd number
- it is nearly 20, 3 less than 20
- it is between 10 and 20 – a 'teen' number
- its digits total 8
- both its digits are odd

Numbers to 100

Cross it out

Adding two 1-digit numbers
Two large dice

Each pair writes two numbers between 2 and 12 on a piece
of paper. Throw both dice and write the numbers on the
board. Choose a child to say the total. Any pair with the
matching number can cross it out. The winners are the first to cross out
both their numbers.

> 4
>
> ☒

Counting chorus

Counting back in tens

Divide the class into four large groups and
assign each group a colour or animal. Point to
a group, and ask them to start counting back
in tens from a number, e.g. *ninety-six, eighty-
six, seventy-six, ...* After a few moments
point to another group, who take over
the count. After a few moments point to
another group ... Practise so that the
change-overs are smooth.

> ninety-six...
> eighty-six...
> seventy-six...

Number of the week

> 100

Sample tasks
- Count in tens forwards to our number and backwards
  from our number.
- Count in ones from 80 to our number.
- Collect 100 pence using different coins, e.g. 10p and 20p
  coins.
- Subtract 10, 20, 40, ... from our number.

Sample facts
- it is the tenth 'ten'
- it is the first 3-digit number
- 100 years is called a century
- it is the number of pennies in £1
- it is the total number of fingers on ten people

Grid

Subtracting 11

Draw a 2 × 5 grid on the board. In the top row write 2-digit numbers at random. Allow the children a few minutes to subtract 11 from each number, to go in the bottom row.

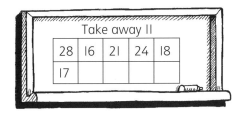

Take away 11				
28	16	21	24	18
17				

Go through the grid on the board asking different pairs for their answers.

Guess what?

Numbers to 100
Number cards (1 to 100)

Choose a child and stick a number card to her back. The rest of the class give clues to help her guess the number, e.g. *It is ten less than 37.*

Each guess costs her 1p. How much does she owe by the time she guesses?

Number of the week

Sample tasks
- Count in fives forwards to our number.
- Count in fives from our number to 50.
- Count in ones backwards from our number to 10.
- Which two 'tens' does our number lie between?
- Add 10 to our number.

Sample facts
- it is an odd number
- it is in the 'fives' – the fifth five
- it is 5 more than 20, 5 less than 30
- its digits total 7
- it has a digit difference of 3

 Addition/subtraction

Jumping jellybean

Ten more

Number cards (1 to 10)

Choose a pair and give them a card. One child jumps ten more times than the number on the card, while the other counts. Are they both correct?

Repeat for different pairs.

Teddy throw

Counting back in tens

Pass the teddy to one child, saying a 2-digit number, e.g. *ninety-eight*. They take the teddy and say the number ten less, i.e. *eighty-eight*. They pass the teddy to another child who says ten less, i.e. *seventy-eight*. Keep passing the teddy like this.

Shape of the week

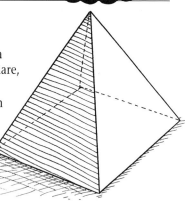

Sample facts
- it has a pointed top
- it has a bottom (its base)
- sometimes its bottom is a triangle, sometimes a square, sometimes other shapes
- it has sloping faces which are triangles
- a pyramid which has a square bottom has 5 faces – 1 square and 4 triangles
- it is the shape of some famous buildings in Egypt, the pyramids.

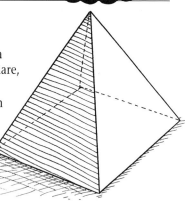

N31 Addition/subtraction

Show me

Subtracting 10 from a teen number
Number cards (0 to 10), one set per pair

Give the children different teen numbers, and ask them to subtract 10 and find the matching card. When you say: *Show me!* they all hold up their cards.

Cross it out

Addition pairs to 10
Number cards (1 to 10)

Each pair writes two numbers between 1 and 10 on a piece of paper. Take a card and choose a child to say what goes with it to make 10. Any pair with the matching number can cross it out.

The winners are the first to cross out both their numbers.

Number of the week

Sample tasks
- Count in twos from 0 to our number, and back.
- Count in tens from our number.
- Add 2, 5, 3, 1, 9, ... to our number.
- What must be added to our number to make 20?
- Take 1, 3, 2, 5, ... away from our number.

Sample facts
- it is odd – the sixth odd number
- it is not a double
- it is a 2-digit number, with both digits the same
- it reads the same both ways round (it is a palindrome)
- it is between 10 and 20, but nearer to 10

N32 Addition and money

My mistake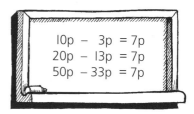

Subtracting from a multiple of 10
Write three subtractions involving
money on the board, one of which is
incorrect.

The children work together in pairs to
decide which one is incorrect. After a
few minutes choose different pairs to answer. Choose one pair to re-write
the addition correctly.

10p – 3p = 7p
20p – 13p = 7p
50p – 33p = 7p

Fast fingers!

Counting in tens
10p coins

Say an amount that is a multiple of 10p, e.g.
seventy pence. Each child holds up fingers to
match that many tens, i.e. seven. Check by
counting out seven 10p coins.

Repeat for different amounts.

Seventy pence

Number of the week

22

Sample tasks
- Count in twos from 2 to our number, and back again.
- Count in ones from our number to 50.
- Write the number which is 2 less, 3 more, ...
- What is double our number (double both the digits)?
- How many more than 20, more than 10 is our number?
- Both its digits are the same. What other numbers are like this?

Sample facts
- it is an even number
- it is double 11
- it is halfway between 20 and 24
- it reads the same both ways round, like 11
- it is more than 20, but less than 25

Addition

Odd one out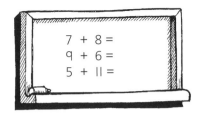

Adding two numbers up to 20
Write three additions on the board, two
of which have the same answer, e.g.
$7 + 8 =$, $9 + 6 =$, $5 + 11 =$.

$$7 + 8 =$$
$$9 + 6 =$$
$$5 + 11 =$$

Allow the pairs a few minutes to decide
which is the 'odd one out'.

Repeat for different additions.

Round the class

Doubling
Point to a child and say a number, e.g. *five*. He responds by saying the
double, i.e. *ten*. He chooses another child (boys choose girls and vice
versa), and says a number, e.g. *three*. She responds by saying the double,
i.e. *six*.

Continue around the class.

Shape of the week

Sample facts
- it is a solid or hollow shape with a pointed top
- it has a circle-shaped (circular) end
- it has a flat end face, and a curved face
- it is the shape of an ice-cream cornet
- it is a pyramid with a circle bottom (base)
- it can be made by rolling a piece of paper

N34 Odd and even

Lose a life

Addition pairs to 10
**Number cards (1 to 10),
one set per pair, cubes**

Give each pair three cubes,
representing three 'lives'. Say a
number, e.g. *six*. Each pair chooses the
card to make ten and, on your cue, holds it
up. Any pair who answers incorrectly loses a
life and must give you a cube.

Repeat.

Jumping jellybean

Odd and even
Number cards (1 to 20)

Choose a pair and give them a card. One child jumps to match the
number on the card, while the other counts. They then say if the number
is odd or even. Are they correct?

Repeat for different pairs.

Number of the week

Sample tasks
- Count in tens from 10 to our number, and beyond.
- Count in fives from 5 to our number, and back.
- What is 10, 30, 50 more than our number?
- Say two pairs of tens which add to make our number, e.g. 10 and 30.
- Take 10, 5, 1, ... from our number.

Sample facts
- it is in the tens – the fourth ten
- it is double 20
- it is in the fives – the eighth five
- it is 10 more than 30, 10 less than 50
- it is the total number of toes on 4 people

N35 Numbers to 100

Grid

Subtracting 11

Draw a 2 × 5 grid on the
board. In the top row write
numbers (up to 20) at random.
Allow the children a few
minutes to double each
number, to go in the bottom row.

Doubles

6	13	12	8	15
12				

Go through the grid on the board asking different pairs for their answers.

Counting chorus

Counting in fives

Divide the class into four large groups and assign
each group a colour or animal. Point to a group,
and ask them to start counting in fives, e.g. *five,
ten, fifteen,* ... After a few moments point to
another group, who take over the count.
After a few moments point to another
group ...

Practise so that the change-overs are
smooth.

*five...
ten...
fifteen...*

Number of the week

50

Sample tasks
- Count in tens from 10 to our number, and beyond.
- Count in fives from 5 to our number, and back.
- Add 5, 9, 12, 21, ... to our number.
- Write 20 less, 10 less, 40 less, ... than our number.

Sample facts
- it is in the tens – the fifth ten
- two 50s make 100 – (it is half of 100)
- it is in the fives – the tenth five
- it is double 25
- it is 10 more than 40

N36 Ordering

Show me

Adding two 1-digit numbers
Number cards (0 to 10), one set per pair

Give the children different additions, and ask them to choose cards to match the answer. When you say: *Show me!* they all hold up their cards. For example:

What is the total of ... five and two, six and four, one and eight, two and seven, four and five?

Teddy throw

Counting in fives

Pass the teddy to one child, saying: *Five*. They take the teddy and say the number five more, i.e. *ten*. They pass the teddy to another child who says five more, i.e. *fifteen*. Keep passing the teddy like this.

Word of the week

opposite

Sample tasks
- What is opposite to left?
- Stand opposite to me.
- Draw a square. Show me which sides are opposite each other.
- Find a rectangle. Which sides are opposite each other?
- Find a dice. Show me a pair of opposite faces.

Sample facts
- left and right are opposite directions
- up and down are opposite movements
- some shapes have opposite sides, e.g. square, rectangle
- a cube has three pairs of opposite faces
- the opposite faces of a dice total 7

Addition

Fast fingers!

Addition pairs to 10

Each child holds up ten fingers. Say a number, e.g. *seven*. The children fold down that many fingers and say how many are still standing, i.e. *three!*

Repeat for different 1-digit numbers, maintaining a brisk pace.

My mistake

Adding 9 to a 1-digit number

Write three additions on the board, one of which is incorrect, e.g. $8 + 9 = 17$, $5 + 9 = 14$, $6 + 9 = 16$. The children work together in pairs to decide which one is incorrect. After a

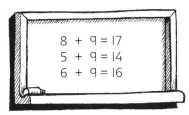

$$8 + 9 = 17$$
$$5 + 9 = 14$$
$$6 + 9 = 16$$

few minutes choose different pairs to answer. Choose one pair to re-write the addition correctly.

Number of the week

21

Sample tasks
- Count in ones to our number, and back from our number.
- Count in twos from 1 to our number.
- What must be added to our number to make 30?
- Add 2, 5, 1, 6, ... to our number.
- Write the number which is 1 less, 1 more than our number.

Sample facts
- it is an odd number
- it is the number of days in three weeks
- it is between 20 and 30, but nearer 20
- it is 1 more than 20, and 9 less than 30
- it is not a double

Subtraction

Cross it out

Counting in fives
Two dice

Each pair writes two fives on a piece of paper, e.g. 20, 45. Throw both dice and, as a class, count that many fives. Any pair with the matching number can cross it out.

The winners are the first to cross out both their numbers.

Grid

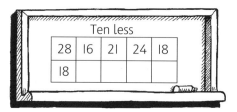

Subtracting 11
Draw a 2 × 5 grid on the board. In the top row write 2-digit numbers at random. Allow the children a few minutes to subtract 10 from each number, to go in the bottom row.

Ten less				
28	16	21	24	18
18				

Go through the grid on the board asking different pairs for their answers.

Shape of the week

cylinder

Sample facts
- it is a solid or hollow shape
- it has two circle end faces
- it has a curved face
- a pipe or a tube is a cylinder shape
- it rolls
- it can be made by rolling a piece of paper

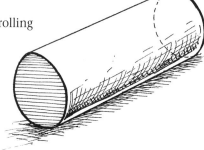

N39 Addition/subtraction

Lose a life

Subtraction problems
Number cards (1 to 10), one set per pair, cubes

Give each pair three cubes, representing three 'lives'. Say a subtraction problem, e.g. *How many do I have left if I start with 20 sweets and eat 5?* Each pair chooses the matching card and, on your cue, holds it up. Any pair who answers incorrectly loses a life and must give you a cube.

Repeat.

Jumping jellybean

Odd and even
Number cards (10 to 20)

Choose a pair and give them a card. One child subtracts 10 and jumps to match the answer, while the other counts. Are they both correct?

Repeat for different pairs.

Word of the week

Sample tasks
- Is 17 an odd number?
- What is the next odd number after 7?
- Say the odd numbers, in order, starting at 1.
- Is the date today an odd number?

Sample facts
- even numbers are the 'twos', the other numbers are odd numbers
- numbers which are not odd are even
- odd numbers have a units digit of 1, 3, 5, 7 or 9
- the first odd number is 1
- odd and even numbers come in turns (they alternate)

Odd one out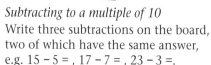

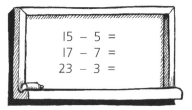

Subtracting to a multiple of 10
Write three subtractions on the board,
two of which have the same answer,
e.g. 15 − 5 = , 17 − 7 = , 23 − 3 =.

Allow the pairs a few minutes to
decide which is the 'odd one out'.

Repeat for different subtractions.

Grid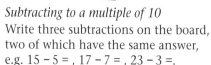

Adding 9 to a 1-digit number
Draw a 2 × 5 grid on the board. In the top row write 1-digit numbers at random. Allow the children a few minutes to add 9 to each number, to go in the bottom row.

Go through the grid on the board asking different pairs for their answers.

Number of the week

Sample tasks
- Count in twos to our number.
- Count in ones from our number to 50.
- Say the number which is 1 more, 1 less.
- Say the number which is 10 more, 10 less.
- The units digit is double the tens digit. Write some other numbers like this, e.g. 12.

Sample facts
- it is an even number
- it is a double – double 12
- it is between 20 and 30, but slightly nearer 20
- it is the number of hours in a day
- it is two twelves – two dozen

N41 Addition/subtraction

My mistake

Adding two numbers up to 30
Write three additions involving money
on the board, one of which is incorrect.
The children work together in pairs to
decide which one is incorrect. After a
few minutes choose different pairs to
answer. Choose one pair to re-write the addition correctly.

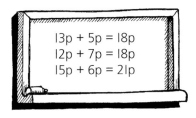

13p + 5p = 18p
12p + 7p = 18p
15p + 6p = 21p

Guess what?

Coin recognition
A selection of coins

Choose a child and stick a coin to his back.
The rest of the class give clues to help him
guess the coin, e.g. *It is silver.*

Each guess costs him 1p. How much does he
owe by the time he guesses?

Number of the week

60

Sample tasks • Count in tens to our number, and beyond our number.
• Count in twos to our number, starting at 20.
• Add 1, 4, 7, ... to our number.
• Say two 'tens' which add to our number, e.g. 40 and 20.
• What is 10 less, 20 less, 50 less, ... than our number?

Sample facts • it is in the tens – the sixth ten
• it is between 50 and 100, but nearer to 50
• it is an even number, because its units digit is zero
• it is a double – double 30

Activity Bank

The Activity Bank includes a variety of activities that address key skills. The activities in the bank can be used at any time alongside any topic, and often you will wish to revisit them throughout the year.

The table lists each activity in the bank, along with the key skill addressed, to help your selection.

Activity	Skill

1. Counting

Choose a child	Counting to 10
Finger surprise	Counting to 10
Silent counting	Counting to 20
At the front	Counting to 20
Stand up!	Counting to 100
Two by two	Counting in twos
Which half?	Counting in twos
Paired up	Counting in twos
Legs out	Counting in tens
Team effort	Counting in tens from a 1-digit number
Out front	Counting in tens from a 1-digit number
Beat the fives	Counting in fives

2. Place-value and ordering

Do as I say!	Comparing numbers up to 30
Larger or not	Comparing numbers up to 30
Stand up, lie down	Comparing numbers up to 20
Show and say	Tens and units
Match mine	Tens and units

3. Adding

Next number	One more
Two more animals	Two more
Team points	Adding two numbers up to 20
Dice count-up	Adding numbers up to 20
Card totals	Adding two numbers up to 20
Unpeg the line	Adding two numbers up to 20
Behind your back	Adding two 1-digit numbers

Activity	Skill
Jump up!	Addition pairs to 10
What's new	Adding multiples of ten
Sit down, stand up	Doubling

4. Subtracting

Whose number?	Counting back one
Match the card	Taking away from a number up to 10
Stand up!	One less
Two less	Two less
What's new?	Taking away 10 from a multiple to 10
Dice count-back	Taking away from a number up to 20

5. Money

Stand to attention!	Coin recognition
Guess the coin	Coin recognition
Two coin total	Amounts of money
Missing coin!	Coin recognition
Coins together	Coin recognition
In my pocket	Total amounts
Buying cakes	Change

6. Solving problems in real life and measures

Animal guess	To estimate lengths and solve problems involving measures
Guess whose tower	To estimate lengths and solve problems involving measures
Bubble sort	To estimate lengths and solve problems involving measures
How many steps?	To estimate lengths and solve problems involving measures
Jugful!	To estimate capacities and solve problems involving measures
What's the time?	To solve problems involving time
Time me jumping!	To solve problems involving time
Weekday challenge	To know and order the days of the week
Month stand-up	To know and order the months of the year

❶ Counting

Choose a child

Counting to 10

Choose ten children to stand in a line, and count along them: *one, two, three, … ten*. Choose a child to point to someone in the line, e.g. Raj. In unison, everyone counts up to that child, e.g. *one, two, … six*.

Finger surprise

Counting to 10

Each child holds their hands behind their back. On your cue, they bring out their hands with a number of fingers showing. Choose numbers at random: How many children are holding up three fingers? Five fingers? Which number appeared most?

Silent counting

Counting to 20

Point to a child who holds up a finger and mouths 'one' without saying it aloud. Point to a second child who holds up two fingers and mouths 'two'. Continue up to ten. Start again at one.

Extend to counting up to twenty.

At the front

Counting to 20
Number cards (1 to 20)

Deal one number card to each of 20 children. Any children without a card stand at the front. These children count slowly from one to twenty. When a child with a card hears their number they stand up.

At the end are there any children still sitting?

Repeat with different children holding the cards.

Stand up!

Counting to 100

Point to a child who says *One*. Point to a second child who says *Two*. Point to a third child who says *Three*. Continue up to ten. That child stands up. Continue counting, quite quickly, up to 100. Each child who says a multiple of ten stands up. How many children are standing?

Two by two

Counting in twos

Each pair chooses to be an animal. Make an 'ark' at the front of the class. Choose a pair – they say their animal and walk to the 'ark'. The class count *Two*. Choose another pair to say their animal and walk to the 'ark'. The class count *Four*. Continue for each pair.

Which half?

Counting in twos

Divide the class into two large groups. One group begins counting *One*. The second group counts *Two*. The first group counts *Three*. Write all the even numbers on one side of the board, and the odd numbers on the other. Continue up to 20.

The children will need practice to do this quickly – help by using the number line.

Paired up

Counting in twos

Count round the class in twos, pointing to one pair at a time, each pair saying the next number in the count *Two, four, six, ...* As each pair says their number they stand up. When everyone is standing, count back in twos, each pair sitting down when they say their number.

Legs out

Counting in tens

Choose ten children to sit on the floor with knees drawn up in front of them – they need space to stretch out their legs. Point to a child, who says *Ten* (ten toes) and quickly stretches out their legs. Point to a second child who says *Twenty* and does the same. Continue up to 100, counting in tens.

Repeat with different children.

Team effort

Counting in tens from a 1-digit number

Divide the class into three teams. Together count in tens starting from a 1-digit number, e.g. *Three, thirteen, twenty-three, ...* After several numbers point to a team who continue the count alone, up to the next number over 100.

Repeat, choosing different teams each time.

Out front

Counting in tens from a 1-digit number

Choose a child to stand at the front. Give the rest of the class a 1-digit starting number, e.g. *Four.* They begin counting in tens *Four, fourteen, twenty-four, ...* At any time the first child can shout *Stop!* They then take over the count to beyond 100. If correct, the rest of the class give them a clap.

Choose another child and repeat.

Beat the fives

Counting in fives

Count in fives as a class: *Five, ten, fifteen, ...*

As each number is said the children hold up five fingers on alternate hands, and slap their knee. This sets up a regular rhythm: *Five* (slap!), *ten* (slap!), *fifteen* (slap!), ...

➋ Place-value and ordering

Do as I say!

Comparing numbers up to 30
Number cards (1 to 30)

Deal one card to each child. Give them a criterion, e.g. *Numbers larger than fifteen*. Children with a number that matches stand up and hold the card for you to see.

Repeat for other criteria, e.g. numbers less than 10, numbers more than 20.

Larger or not

Comparing numbers up to 30
Number cards (1 to 30)

Deal one card to each child. Point
to two children who stand up,
with their numbers hidden (e.g.
held to their chests). The rest
of the class guess who has the
larger number. The two
children reveal their numbers.
Who was correct?

Continue, for different
pairs.

Stand up, lie down

Comparing numbers up to 20
Each child thinks of a number
between 1 and 20 and
writes it down. Point to
a number on the line,
e.g. 16. All the
children with a
larger number
stand up; all the
children with a
smaller number lie
down. Is anyone
still sitting?

Repeat for
different numbers
on the line.

Show and say

Tens and units
Place-value cards (Ts and Us)

Deal one card at random
to each child. Each child
with a tens card must
pair up with a child with
units card. Choose
different pairs to hold
up their cards and say
their number. Are
they correct?

Repeat for each pair.

Match mine

Tens and units
Number grid (1 to 100)

Each child thinks of a number up to 100 and writes it down.

Point to the first row the grid
and count along it in unison
One, two, three, …

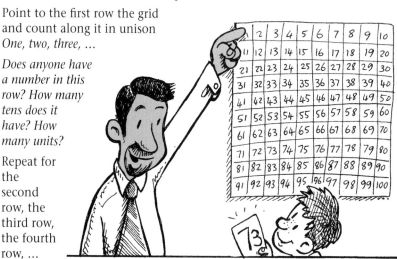

*Does anyone have
a number in this
row? How many
tens does it
have? How
many units?*

Repeat for
the
second
row, the
third row,
the fourth
row, …

❸ Adding

Next number

One more
Number line (1 to 20)

Each pair takes one number from the line. Choose a pair: Count up to your number, e.g. *One, two, three, ... six. Who has one more than six?* The pair with 7 hold up their card and shout out *Seven*, as quickly as possible.

Repeat, starting with different pairs.

Two more animals

Two more

Choose a child and say an animal, e.g. *Duck*. That child quacks once.

Choose another child and say a different animal, e.g. *Dog*. That child barks two more than the last child (i.e. three times).

Choose another child and say a different animal, e.g. *Cat*. That child miaows two more than the last child (i.e. five times).

Continue up to about ten, then start again from one.

Team points

Adding two numbers up to 20

Divide the children into two teams. Write the odd numbers 1 to 19 on the board for one team and the even numbers 2 to 20 for the other.

Choose one child from each team to stand at the front with their hands behind their backs. On your cue, they both bring their hands out with a number of fingers standing up. With the class add the two numbers to find the total, e.g. 11. The team with that number score a point.

Repeat with different children, until one team has three points (i.e. evens).

Dice count-up

Adding numbers up to 20

Sets of number cards (2 to 12), two dice, cubes

Deal one card to each child. Throw both dice and call out the numbers. Choose a child to say the total. Any children with the matching card can collect a cube.

Repeat, until one child has three cubes.

Card totals

Adding two numbers up to 20

Two sets of number cards (1 to 10), cubes

Spread out all the cards face down. Each pair chooses a number from 2 to 20 and writes it down. Select two cards and hold them up. Choose a child to say the total. Any pair with that number can collect a cube.

Replace the cards and repeat. At the end of several rounds, who has the most cubes?

Unpeg the line

Adding two numbers up to 20

Sets of number cards (1 to 10)

Deal one card to each child. They then arrange themselves in pairs, and find the total of their two cards.

Point to a number on the line, e.g. 6. *Does any pair have this total?* Place the card on the floor, so that all pairs with a matching total can sit around it.

Repeat for different numbers. Are there any left on the line?

Behind your back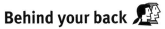

Adding two 1-digit numbers

Cubes

Write four numbers on the board, e.g. 6, 8, 10, 12.

Each pair puts their hands behind their backs. On your cue, each pair brings out both hands with some fingers showing. What is each pair's total? Any pair with a total that matches one of the numbers on the board collects a cube.

Repeat.

Jump up!

Addition pairs to 10
Sets of number cards (0 to 9), two dice

Deal one card to each child. Throw
one or two dice (if you throw 11 or
12, throw again) and choose a
child to say the total. Any child
with a card that goes with the
total to make 10 stands
up, holding their
card. Write the pair
of numbers on the
board.

Repeat.

What's new?

Adding multiples of ten

Point to a child, who says a multiple of ten, e.g. *Thirty*. Point to another
child who adds 20, and says the answer, i.e. *Fifty*. If correct the second
child says a new multiple of ten. Choose another child to add 20.

Continue around the class.

Sit down, stand up

Doubling

Number line (1 to 20)

One child in each pair stands up, the other stays seated. Point to a number on the line, e.g. 3. The seated children clap that many times in unison and say the number. The standing children double the number and clap a matching number of times, saying the answer *Six*. Rehearse together *Three and three makes six*.

Repeat for different numbers, with children swapping roles.

④ Subtracting

Whose number?

Counting back one

Sets of number cards (1 to 10), number line (1 to 10)

Deal one card to each child, which they keep hidden. Point to a number on the line and choose a child to say it, then count back one. Any child with the matching number stands up and gives their card to you. Give them a new card, and repeat the whole process.

Match the card

Taking away from a number up to 10
Sets of number cards (1 to 10), a cloth bag, cubes

Deal one card to each child. Choose a child to count ten cubes into the bag *One, two, three, … ten.*

Remove two cubes and show the class. *How many are left?*

Choose a child to answer (they can use fingers to help). Does anyone have a matching card? Replace the cubes and remove a different number.

Stand up!

One less
Sets of number cards (1 to 20), a teddy or other soft toy

Deal one card to each child. Give one child the teddy. They stand up and read their number aloud. Any child with the number one less stands up and reads their number aloud. If correct one of them chooses another child, who is given the teddy. They stand up and read their number aloud. Again, any child with the number one less stands up and reads their number aloud. Continue.

Two less

Two less

Choose a child and say an animal, e.g. *Duck*. That child quacks ten times.

Choose another child and say a different animal, e.g. *Cat*. That child miaows two less than the last child (i.e. eight times).

Choose another child and say a different animal, e.g. *Cow*. That child moos two less than the last child (i.e. six times).

Continue to zero, then start again from a different starting number.

What's new?

Taking away 10 from a multiple of 10

Point to a child, who says a multiple of ten, e.g. *thirty*. Point to another child who subtracts 10, and says the answer, i.e. *twenty*. If correct the second child says a new multiple of ten. Choose another child to subtract 10.

Continue around the class.

Dice count-back

Taking away from a number up to 20

Sets of number cards (0 to 17), two dice, cubes

Write a starting number on the board, between 11 and 20. Deal one card to each child.

Throw both dice and choose a child to subtract the total from the starting number (using a number line to help).

Any children with a card that matches the answer can collect a cube.

Repeat for different starting numbers, until one child has three cubes.

❺ Money

Stand to attention!

Coin recognition

A selection of coins (1p, 2p, 5p, 10p, 20p)

Give each child a coin. In unison, count from 1 to 20. When a number is spoken that matches a child's coin they stand up, holding their coin. When you reach 20, count back, with children sitting down as their amount is said.

Guess the coin

Coin recognition

A selection of coins (1p, 2p, 5p, 10p, 20p)

Give each of five children a different coin, hidden from the rest of the class. The class give instructions to the five children, to help them guess the coins, e.g. the child with the coin worth the most should jump in the air. Any child with a brown coin should sit down. Any child with a silver coin should shout their name.

Two coin total

Amounts of money
A selection of coins (1p, 2p, 5p, 10p), number line (1 to 20)

Give each child a coin. Each pair must work out their total.

Count, in unison, along the number line *One, two, three, ...* As each pair's total is said, they stand up. Continue until every pair is standing.

Missing coin!

Coin recognition
Coins (1p to £2, one of each)

Place the coins on a tray, and rehearse the recognition and value of each one. Ask all the children to shut their eyes, and remove a coin.

When they open their eyes can they guess which coin is missing? Reveal the coin. *Who was correct? How did they guess?*

Replace the coin and repeat.

Variation: Replace the missing coin with a different coin.

Coins together

Coin recognition
Coins (5p, 10p, 20p, 50p)

Choose two children and give them each a coin, hidden from the rest of the class. The two children take turns to describe their coin, e.g. it is not round, it is small. The class guess what the two coins are, and hence the total. Write some totals on the board.

The two children reveal their coins. *What were they? What is the total? Did anyone guess correctly?* Repeat with different children.

In my pocket

Total amounts
Tell the children stories about coins you have in your pocket (use real coins, if possible).

In my pocket I have two coins. One is brown, one is silver. How much could I have? The children work in pairs to suggest different totals. Discuss the possibilities. Repeat for three coins.

Buying cakes 🗣

Change
Coins (1p, 2p, 5p, 10p)

Give each pair a coin: 1p, 2p, 5p or 10p.

The cake costs 7p. Write '7p' on the board. *Who cannot afford to buy the cake?* The pairs with 2p or 5p should stand up.

Choose some of the children still sitting. *How much change would you get if you bought it?* Check with the class.

Repeat for different items and prices.

⑥ Solving problems in real life and measures

Animal guess

To estimate lengths and solve problems involving measures

Say to the children: *I am thinking of an animal. It is about two hand-spans tall. What animal might I be thinking of?*

Let children guess and, if necessary, give them a clue by making the animal noise. Play again. *I am thinking of a creature. It is about 1 cm long and it has six legs.*

Play again, sometimes choosing standard units and sometimes choosing non-standard units to describe the size of the creature. Sometimes describe its height and sometimes its length.

Guess whose tower

To estimate lengths and solve problems involving measures

Interlocking cubes, string or ribbon, scissors

Each pair builds a tower of cubes of between 2 and 20 cubes tall.

Cut a piece of string and hold it up. Ask for pairs who think their tower is the same length as the string. Compare with those pairs. Whose tower is closest? They score a point.

Play again with different towers and lengths of string. Encourage the children to estimate whether their tower is the same length as your string (or longer or shorter).

Bubble sort

To estimate lengths and solve problems involving measures

Choose ten children to stand in a line, in plenty of space (they should be in no particular order). Point at the two children on the left-hand side of the line. Consult the class: *Look at Sharon and Jamie. Who is taller? Jamie.*

Swap those children so that the taller child (Jamie) is on the right-hand side of the pair. Now look at Jamie and the next child. Who is taller? Swap those two around so that the taller child is on the right. Continue, comparing pairs until you reach the end of the line. Start again from the left-hand side of the line, and repeat the process until all the children are in order of height, smallest to largest. Check with the class.

How many steps?

To estimate lengths and solve problems involving measures
Choose a child to stand in a place where the class can see them.

Consult the class: *How many steps from here to the door?* The children work in pairs to guess and write their guesses on a piece of paper. The child walks to the door slowly, and the class count her steps. Whose guess was closest?

Repeat, with different children starting in different places.

Jugful!

To estimate capacities and solve problems involving measures
A large jug and lots of small cubes

Hold up the jug. *How many cubes do you think will fill the jug?* Ask each pair to guess and record them on the board.

Fill the jug, counting the cubes in fives or twos. Stop when it is half full. *How many cubes have we used? Does anyone want to change their guess?* Allow pairs to change if they wish.

Continue filling until the jug is full. How many cubes? Whose guess was closest?

What's the time?

To solve problems involving time
Number cards (0 to 12), one set for each child

Draw a large analogue clock face on the board. Draw the minute hand pointing to 12 o'clock. The children have to guess the time, from your clues, e.g. *It is the time we usually go home* (e.g. 3 o'clock). The children hold up card '3' to show you.

Play again, for different clues and times.

Time me jumping!

To solve problems involving time
A minute timer

Choose a child. Consult the class: *How many times do you think Sam can jump in one minute?* The children work in pairs to guess. Record each pair's guess on the board. Start the timer and the child starts jumping. The class counts in unison (the first child must jump deliberately and fairly slowly). At the end of the minute how many jumps has he made? Whose guess was closest?

Repeat.

Weekday challenge

To know and order the days of the week
Day cards (Monday, Tuesday, ...) one for each pair, a dice, cubes

Throw the dice and write the number on the board, e.g. 5. *What is the fifth day of the week?* Start chanting the days from Monday: *Monday, Tuesday, ... Friday. Friday is the fifth day of the week.*

Any pair with a Friday card can take a cube.

Throw the dice again and repeat. If two consecutive dice throws are the same, then children with 'Sunday' cards can collect a cube.

Repeat until every pair has at least two cubes.

Month stand-up

To know and order the months of the year
Month cards (January, February, ...) one for each child

Deal the cards, one to each child. In unison, chant the months of the year. As each month is said, any child holding that card can stand up.

At the end of the chant is everyone standing? Repeat the chanting, this time with children sitting down as their month is said.

Skills Chart

The following chart outlines all the mental skills addressed by the Mental Warm-up activities. The skills are divided into three key areas: *counting and place-value, addition, subtraction* and *money*.

The chart will assist any teacher looking for an activity dealing with a specific skill. It also makes clear the build-up and sequence of concepts covered throughout the book.

Topic	Specific skills	Units
Counting and place-value	Counting to 20	N1, N2, N7, N9, N15, N23
	Counting in twos	N8, N9, N20, N21
	Counting in fives	N35, N36, N38
	Counting in tens	N7, N12, N15, N27, N32
	Counting back in ones	N1, N24
	Counting back in tens	N28, N30
	Number names up to ten	N2
	Numbers to 20	N4, N21
	Numbers to 30	N10
	Numbers to 50	N16
	Numbers to 100	N29
	Odd and even	N22, N34, N39
Addition	Adding two 1-digit numbers	N3, N4, N8, N11, N19, N28, N36
	Adding two 1-digit numbers, crossing 10	N12, N18
	Adding 10 to a 1-digit number	N14, N20, N22
	Adding 10 to a teen number	N13
	Adding two numbers up to 20	N33
	Adding two numbers up to 30	N41
	Addition pairs to 10	N14, N16, N18, N19, N24, N25, N26, N31, N34, N37
	Adding three 1-digit numbers	N25
	Ten more	N3, N30

	Adding 9 to a 1-digit number	N37, N40
	Doubling	N5, N17, N33
	Adding and subtracting	N17, N23, N26
Subtraction	Taking away from a number up to 10	N5, N10, N27
	Taking away from a number up to 20	N11
	Subtracting 10 from a teen number	N31
	Subtracting from a multiple of 10	N32
	Subtracting to a multiple of 10	N40
	Subtracting 11	N29, N35, N38
	Subtraction problems	N39
Money	Coin recognition	N6, N13, N41
	Adding 1p to amounts	N6